THE NUCLEAR CASEBOOK
—An Illustrated Guide—

by Dr. C. Phillips and Dr. I. Ross

Polygon Books

First published 1983.

Revised edition published 1984 by
Polygon Books,
1 Buccleuch Place, Edinburgh EH8 9LW.

Copyright © 1983, 1984 C. Phillips and I. Ross.

Typeset by EUSPB.

Colour reproduction by CMR Graphics, East Kilbride.

Printed by McQueen Printers, Galashiels.

ISBN 0 904919 83 8

Acknowledgments

This book has been very much a collaborative effort.
Cover design: Jenny Phillips based on 'The False Mirror' by Rene Magritte.
Art Work: Jenny Phillips and David Simon.
Cartoonists: Raymond Briggs and Mel Calman.
Word Processing by hand: Mrs P. Hunter and C. A. Mackenzie et al.
The Friendly Ear; Neville Moir of Polygon Books.
MCANW: For the original literature search on the medical effects: Dr Frank Boulton, Dr Christine Dean, Dr Nigel Hurst, Professor J. R. S. Fincham, Dr Ken Jones, Dr Christopher Ludlam, Dr Ian McCarthy, Dr Judith McDonald, Dr Shirley Ratcliffe, Dr Maureen Roberts, Dr Brian Venters, and Dr Helen Zeally.
For critical reading of the text, Margaret Fraser, Dr Shirley Ratcliffe, Dr Nigel Hurst, Andrea Joyce.
IPPNW: Professor Robert Jay Lifton and Dr K. Erikson.
SANA: Dr Alan Longman, Professor Michael Pentz, Dr Assam Quisrawi, Dr Philip Steadman, David Simmonds, Stuart Swanson and Alan Walker.
Others: Dr Hector Cameron, Nigel Mace and Duncan Campbell and his public spirited moles.
We would also like to thank: Wildwood House Ltd for the use of pictures from *Unforgettable Fire*; Hamish Hamilton Ltd for the use of cartoons from Raymond Briggs' *When The Wind Blows*; Research Institute for Nuclear Medicine and Biology, Hiroshima University for the photograph of a man dying from Radiation Sickness; Shogo Yamahata for the Hiroshima photographs on pages 5 and 44 taken by his Father Yosuke Yamahata; Professor G. Melvyn Howe for the use of smallpox photograph.

For Anna and Barnaby
and all the other children born into this World.

Contents

Introduction

During the 1981 Edinburgh International Festival the Medical Campaign Against Nuclear Weapons (MCANW) mounted an exhibition illustrating the medical effects of nuclear war. Subsequently, many requests were made for copies of this exhibition and it was felt that it would be helpful to have a book which people could take home to read at leisure. In producing this book, however, we have added a great deal of new material and so we hope that it will be useful whether or not the exhibition has been seen.

When we began work on the 1981 exhibition we started from a position of relative ignorance, but rapidly came to realise that nuclear weapons produce destruction and loss of life on a scale which is hard to comprehend and for which there could be no effective medical response. This conclusion is confirmed in the 1983 BMA Report:

> "The explosion of a single nuclear bomb of the size used at Hiroshima over a major city in the UK is likely to produce so many cases of trauma and burns requiring treatment that the remaining services in the UK would be completely overwhelmed."[1]

Many people still adhere to the belief that nuclear war can only be prevented by continuing to deploy newer and more sophisticated weapons. We, and others, believe this is a tragic misconception of the real nature of the arms race. During the last decade there have been many technological advances, particularly in the field of missile accuracy, and many impartial analysts believe that these innovations are undermining the security and stability that was believed to result from nuclear deterrence. An understanding of these factors is crucial to the whole debate and so are dealt with in some depth (pp 10-21).

We have also given considerable space to illustrate the work of Openshaw and Steadman (Scientists Against Nuclear Weapons—SANA) who were the first to undertake a detailed investigation of discrepancies in the Home Office's estimates for casualties following a nuclear attack. While this section does not address the fundamental question as to how we can prevent a nuclear war it does throw doubt on the integrity of some official statements.

In this second edition, apart from some minor changes, we have added two further sections. The first describes the newly discovered phenomenon, the "Nuclear Winter"; the second describes a new approach to multilateral disarmament based on a paper by Stephen Salter which is to be published in *Scientific American*.

Since nuclear weapons have potentially indiscriminate effects on defenceless civilians many feel that even their threatened use can never be justified. None the less, there seems to be good evidence to suggest that recent developments have made a mockery of the concept of nuclear deterrence and that the present policies are leading down a road to destruction.

However, you the reader must examine the evidence we present and draw your own conclusions.

We are greatly indebted to all those who have helped directly or indirectly to produce this book and a full list of acknowledgements appears on the title page. Any errors or omissions are our responsibility.

Crispin Phillips, B.Sc., Ph.D.
Molecular Biologist,
Research Associate at the
Centre for Human Ecology.

Ian R. F. Ross, M.B., Ch.B.
General Medical Practitioner,
Part-time Lecturer in General Practice,
University of Edinburgh.

Contact Address: **Centre for Human Ecology,
University of Edinburgh,
15 Buccleuch Place,
Edinburgh EH8 9LN.**

May 1984.

Human history has been interspersed by wars, and for many centuries war has been accepted as an ultimate means, legitimate or otherwise, of resolving major differences between nations.

Following the Napoleonic Wars the Prussian strategist, Carl von Clausewitz, wrote a treatise "On War",[2] a work which is still considered relevant in military circles. Clausewitz saw war as a rational instrument of national policy. However, Clausewitz lived at a time when armies were relatively small and their destructive power was limited.

By 1900 the potential for destruction had increased greatly and as a result, the Hague Convention of 1907 attempted to set limits to war in order to spare civilian populations and limit destruction. Although the Convention was essentially honoured in the 1914-18 War,[3] the indiscriminate bombing of cities and civilian populations by both sides during the Second World War was clearly in breach of the 1907 Hague Convention. Such bombing could only be achieved by major military operations — for example Dresden was devastated in February 1945 by bombs from 1,083 aircraft.[4]

In contrast on Monday, 6th August 1945, a single B-29 bomber dropped one atom bomb and destroyed a whole city — Hiroshima. War had become unlimited and potentially unlimitable.

Kizo Kawakami age 71

Masato Yamashita age 52

August 9
   With no one to help her, a girl died leaning on the bank of the Enko River.

   The following reproductions are from paintings by Hiroshima Survivors 30 years after the event. The full collection of paintings can be seen in *Unforgettable Fire*, published originally by Nippon Hoso Shuppan Kyokai, Tokyo, (and in Britain by:- Wildwood House, Ltd., Gloucester Mansions, Cambridge Circus, London).

turning point

Name unknown, housewife

At Meiji Bridge

A mother, driven half-mad, while looking for her child, was calling his name. At last she found him. His head looked like a boiled octopus. His eyes were half-closed, and his mouth was white, pursed, and swollen.

Kazuo Matsumuro died in 1977.

On the stairs in front of the statue of Fleet Admiral Kato in Hijiyama Park.

Although we were lying side by side we did not recognise each other. He heard my voice and said, "Are you Mr Matsumuro?" It was Mr Yoshimoto. His face was dark and swollen. He seemed unable to open his eyes or mouth. The left side of his face, neck, and hands were burned. Soon we were separated.

I was bleeding from my ears, nose, and mouth and was wounded from being crushed. I learned later that the twelfth backbone and the first lumbar vertebra were fractured. I could hardly move.

7

Civilian and Military Casualties

European

World Wars I and II

Nuclear War 19?? — a few hours later

World Wars I and II

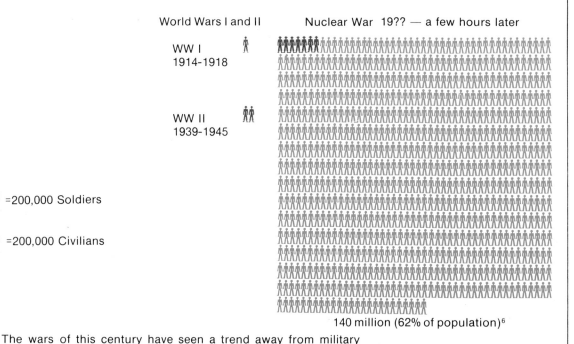

WW I
1914-1918

WW II
1939-1945

WW I

WW II

=200,000 Soldiers

=200,000 Civilians

140 million (62% of population)[6]

The wars of this century have seen a trend away from military casualties towards civilian casualties. The ratio of military to civilian deaths were:[8]

World War 1   20:1 (ie 20 military deaths for 1 civilian death)
World War 2   1:1
Korea   1:5
Vietnam   1:20
Nuclear War   1:100+

In a nuclear war the majority of civilians will be casualties[6] [7]. Therefore, it is vital for each of us to have a clear understanding of the policies upon which our lives depend.

in Twentieth Century Wars

War Deaths[5][7][8]

Nuclear War

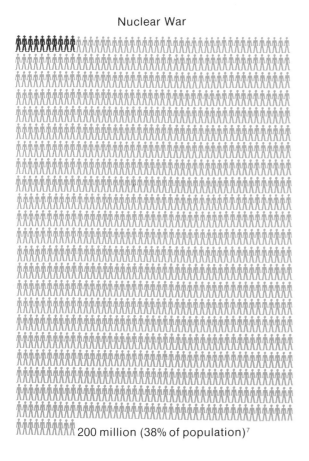

200 million (38% of population)[7]

Soviet War Deaths [5][6][8]

World Wars I and II

WW I

WW II

Nuclear War

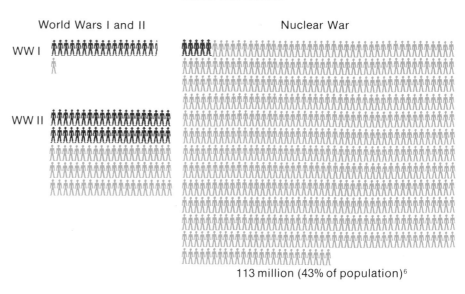

113 million (43% of population)[6]

Nowhere is the bitter experience of the last war felt more keenly
than in the Soviet Union.
Soviet Union[5][8] lost 1 person in 8.
Britain[5] lost 1 person in 130
United States[5] lost 1 person in 325.

Diminishing returns in absurdity

Destruction and Weapon Yield

A 1 kiloton nuclear bomb releases the explosive energy of a thousand (1000) tons of TNT.
A 1 megaton nuclear bomb releases the explosive energy of a million (1,000,000) tons of TNT.

However, it should be realised that the amount of damage caused by a nuclear weapon does not increase in direct proportion to its explosive power. This is a consequence of "volume geometry".

For example, a 1 megaton bomb divided into ten smaller 100 kiloton bombs would cause blast damage twice that of the original 1 megaton bomb.

The Destruction of Deterrence

On August 6th 1945, the 12.5 kiloton nuclear bomb which was dropped on Hiroshima killed between 78,000 and 100,000[10].

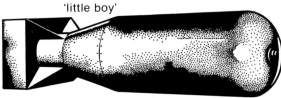
'little boy'

Today the combined arsenals of both superpowers are in excess of sixteen thousand megatons, equivalent to nearly 1.5 million Hiroshima bombs[11][12]. However, when the size of the various bombs are taken into account, the destructive power is somewhat less and equivalent to just over three hundred thousand Hiroshima bombs. This is illustrated on the opposite page.

In an industrialised country a large proportion of the population live in cities and large towns[9][13]. The use of nuclear weapons make the destruction of these population centres relatively easy. However, as the targets become smaller and more numerous, such as towns and villages, so more and more weapons are required for their destruction, but with less and less effect. This point was made clear in a Pentagon study carried out in the 1960's which found that maximum levels of destruction to the Soviet Union could be achieved with about 400 megatons and thereafter the damage inflicted by further bombs had little impact (see graph)[14].

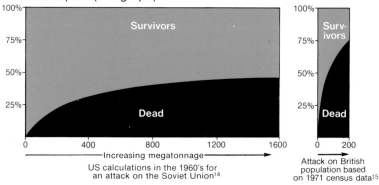

US calculations in the 1960's for an attack on the Soviet Union[14]

Attack on British population based on 1971 census data[15]

The possession today of 16,000 megatons by the superpowers is thus greatly in excess of that required for deterrence. What is the purpose of this vast destructive power? The answer is that our strategy of nuclear deterrence based on the threat of unacceptable damage has been replaced by a new strategy known as COUNTER FORCE.

	Strategic[11][12] Nuclear Weapons		Theatre & Tactical[11] Nuclear Weapons		Total Arsenal	
1982	Number of Warheads	Megatons	Number of Warheads	Megatons	Number of Warheads	Megatons
USA	9,500	3,500	14,343	5,300	23,843	8,800
USSR	8,800	4,500	5,763	3,100	12,420	7,600

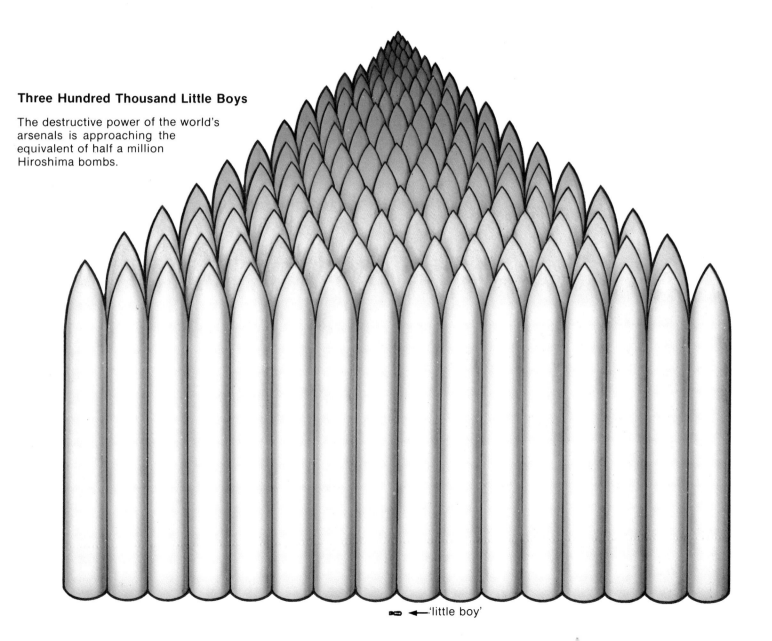

Three Hundred Thousand Little Boys

The destructive power of the world's arsenals is approaching the equivalent of half a million Hiroshima bombs.

◄— 'little boy'

Evolution of Weapons

Since the early 1960's nuclear deterrence has been based on the concept of Mutually Assured Destruction (MAD). Both super-powers realised that although each could launch a devastating attack neither side could destroy the others ability to retaliate in an equally devastating manner. The stability and security of MAD depended therefore upon two factors:

i) The ability to destroy each others cities;
ii) The inability to destroy each others missiles.

However, the development of COUNTERFORCE STRATEGY, which depends upon being able to destroy the other sides missiles in their silos, has undermined the very essence of the MAD doctrine and made nuclear war more likely. The importance of missile accuracy for the implementation of COUNTERFORCE STRATEGY[16] is illustrated on this page.

Destruction of a hardened missile silo depends more upon warhead accuracy than upon megatonnage.

Accuracy is defined as the radius of a circle within which a warhead has a 50% chance of landing and is known as the circular error probable (CEP).

EVOLUTION OF SOVIET WEAPONS

	SSN5 (SLBM)	SS 8 (ICBM)	SS 9 (ICBM)	SSN 8 (SLBM)	SS 19 (ICBM)	SS 17 (ICBM)	SSN 18 (SLBM)	SS 18 mod 4 (ICBM)	SSNX20 (SLBM)	NEW (ICBM)	SS2 (IMR)
SLBM Submarine launched ballistic missile											
ICBM Inter continental ballistic missile											
IMRBM Intermediate range ballistic missile											
ACLM Air launched Cruise missile											
Date of deployment	**1963**	**1963**	**1966**	**1973**	**1976**	**1977**	**1977**	**1979**	**1983**		19
Range in nautical miles	700	6,000	6500	4300	5000	5400	4050	5500	4500		27
Number of warheads	1×Mt	1×5 Mt	1×20 Mt	1×1 Mt	6×0.5 Mt	4×0.5 Mt	3×0.2 Mt	10×0.5 Mt	....	?	3×15
Accuracy (CEP)	1½ miles	1 mile	¾ mile	½ mile	1500 ft	1200 ft	½ mile	950 ft	....		132
Probability of destroying hardened target	1%	3%	37%	11%	26%	39%	3%	50%	....		10

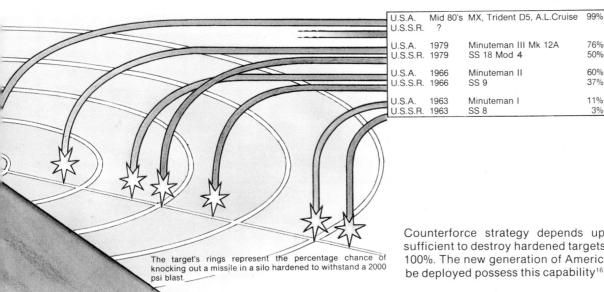

U.S.A.	Mid 80's	MX, Trident D5, A.L.Cruise	99%
U.S.S.R.	?		
U.S.A.	1979	Minuteman III Mk 12A	76%
U.S.S.R.	1979	SS 18 Mod 4	50%
U.S.A.	1966	Minuteman II	60%
U.S.S.R.	1966	SS 9	37%
U.S.A.	1963	Minuteman I	11%
U.S.S.R.	1963	SS 8	3%

The target's rings represent the percentage chance of knocking out a missile in a silo hardened to withstand a 2000 psi blast.

Counterforce strategy depends upon weapons with accuracies sufficient to destroy hardened targets with a probability approaching 100%. The new generation of American weapons which are about to be deployed possess this capability[16].

EVOLUTION OF AMERICAN WEAPONS [19] [20]

...hing II (RBM)	MX (ICBM)	Trident D5 (SLBM)	Air launched Cruise missile (ALCM)	Minuteman III Mk 12A (ICBM)	Trident C4 (SLBM)	Minuteman III (ICBM)	Poseidon C3 (SLBM)	Minuteman II (ICBM)	Polaris A3 (SLBM)	Minuteman I (ICBM)	Titan II (ICBM)	Polaris A1 (SLBM)
...983	Mid 80's	Mid 80's	1983	1979	1979	1970	1970	1966	1964	1963	1962	1960
...70	6000	6000	1350	7000	4000	7000	2500	7000	2500	6500	6300	1200
...25 Mt	14×0.35/0.5Mt	7×0.475 Mt	1×0.2 Mt	3×0.35 Mt	8×0.1 Mt	3×0.17 Mt	10×0.04 Mt	1×1.5 Mt	3×0.2 Mt	1×1 Mt	1 x 9 Mt	1×1 Mt
...0 ft	300 ft	400 ft	200 ft	650 ft	1600 ft	980 ft	1700 ft	1300 ft	½ mile	½ mile	¾ mile	1 mile
...0%	99%	99%	100%	76%	10%	30%	6%	60%	5%	11%	23%	3%

13

Counterforce strategy, which threatens enemy hardened targets such as missile silos, requires the ability to deliver nuclear warheads with great accuracy. The strategy also requires missiles with multiple independently targetable warheads.

e.g. Suppose each side had 100 missiles each with a single warhead. A successful counterforce attack would require that each warhead explodes on target destroying all of the enemies missiles, for otherwise the enemy could retaliate with any remaining missiles.

If however, each side had 100 missiles, each with 10 independently targetable warheads, then one side could launch a counterforce attack using only half of its missiles. In such an attack involving 500 warheads, each of the enemy's missiles would be targeted with 5 warheads thus increasing the probability of their destruction. Even if a few of the enemy's missiles were not destroyed the attacker would still have unused missiles targeted on the enemy's cities to deter retaliation.

USSR			
Year	Strategic* Lethality	Major Weapon	Contribution of major weapon to Lethality
1965	1,037	SS9	61%
1970	6,037	SS9	71%
1975	7,094	SS9	61%
1980	42,284	SS18 & 19	41 & 42%
1985	??,???	SS18 & 19	?? & ??%

The two tables show that increases in lethality are principally brought about by the deployment of new types of weapons.

* Bombers are not included in the lethality calculation because they are slow and vunerable to air defence.

1965
1970
1975
1980

U.S.A. U.S.S.R.

Increase in Strategic Lethality (10^4) 1 2 3 4

USA			
Year	Strategic* Lethality	Major Weapon	Contribution of major weapon to Lethality
1965	4,716	Minuteman I	68%
1970	19,375	Minuteman II	77%
1975	41,520	Minuteman III	47%
1980	43,549	Minuteman III	45%
1985	833,450	Cruise (ALCM)	90%

A measure of counterforce capability is the LETHALITY of the strategic arsenals which takes into account not only the number and yield of the nuclear warheads on ballistic* missiles but also their accuracy.

The illustration on the opposite page shows the lethality of the superpowers strategic arsenals at five year intervals from 1965 to 1980, (also see tables). The illustration at the bottom of this page shows the dramatic increase in lethality of the US strategic arsenal as a result of deploying cruise missiles (note increase in scale).

It can be argued that since cruise missiles are relatively slow they are not weapons of surprise, essential for a counterforce strategy. However because of their long range and invisibility to air defences they have been included in the lethality calculation for 1985. From 1985 onward the US plan to deploy MX and trident D5 ballistic missiles whose accuracies approach that of cruise missiles.

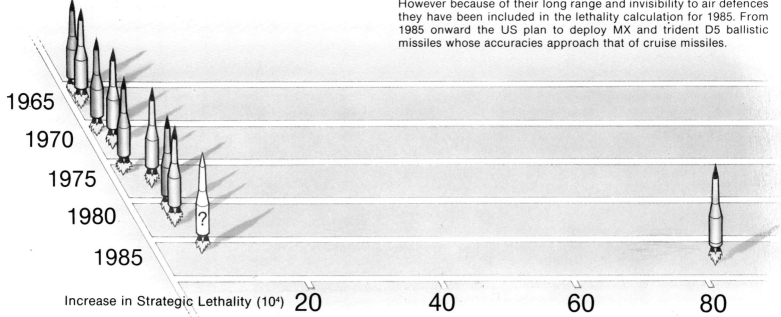

1965

1970

1975

1980

1985

Increase in Strategic Lethality (10⁴) 20   40   60   80

Counterforce strategy and the erosion of deterrence

The doctrine of MUTUALLY ASSURED DESTRUCTION (MAD) arose as a result of the deployment in the 1960's of nuclear ballistic missiles against which neither side had any effective defence.

The MAD doctrine reflected the available technology; thus Intercontinental Ballistic Missiles (ICBM) were only accurate enough to destroy large targets such as cities, and smaller targents such as missile silos were relatively safe. This situation was stable, even in times of crisis, because although each superpower had the ability to destroy the other's cities it was deterred from this as it would inevitably have led to the destruction of its own cities. The development of very accurate warheads which can destroy the other side's missiles in their silos has given rise to a strategy called COUNTERFORCE which renders deterrence obsolete.

In addition to accuracy the other component of a COUNTER-FORCE strategy is the possession of missiles with multiple warheads which are independently targetable.

The large increase in the number of nuclear warheads (shown on pp 18-19) is partly due to the deployment of new missiles during the 60's and 70's but mainly due to their conversion to multiple warheads reflecting the implementation of counterforce strategy. Counterforce strategy was first made public in 1974 in a Congressional Hearing by US Defence Secretary Schlesinger and the doctrine was affirmed by Carter in his Presidential Directive 59 (1980).

USA leads the way

The USA has always had a considerable lead in counterforce capability (pp 13-15). In 1970 the US deployed the Minuteman III which was the first ICBM to have multiple independently targetable warheads. In addition these missiles could deliver their warheads with greater accuracy than before (CEP 980 ft)[14]. It was another five years (1975) before the USSR could deploy an ICBM with multiple independently targetable warheads — the SS19. However the accuracy of these warheads (CEP 1500 ft) was no better than the ten year old US Minuteman II (CEP 1300 ft)[19].

Today while the USSR are deploying the present generation of strategic nuclear weapons the US are about to leave the Soviets far behind by deploying the next generation of counterforce weapons (pp 12-15).

COUNTERFORCE JUSTIFIED

Counterforce — a psychological strategy

The justification of counterforce strategy by the US Defence Department is interesting. It is argued that if the USSR launched a first strike against US missile silos they would keep back a significant proportion of their silo based missiles to be targeted on US cities so as to deter retaliation. Therefore, for the US to retaliate against Soviet cities as demanded by the MAD doctrine, it would be necessary to destroy those silo based missiles. This was called "Second Strike Counterforce Capability" by the Defence Department. The destabilising nature of this strategy was emphasised in a 1978 Congressional Budget Office background paper[21]:

. . . There may be an inescapable dilemma in the procurement of second strike counterforce capability: a US arsenal large enough to attack Soviet ICBMs after having absorbed a first strike would be large enough to threaten the Soviet ICBM force in a US first strike. Moreover, the Soviet Union looking at capabilities rather than intentions, might see a US second-strike capability in this light. Faced with a threat to their ICBM force, Soviet leaders facing an international crisis might have an incentive to use their missiles in a pre-emptive all out strike before they could be destroyed by the United States.

# of Strategy

Counterforce — a military strategy

One justification for adopting a counterforce strategy was the belief that the MAD doctrine was not a credible deterrent in protecting vital US interests. The Soviets might consider that a conventional war in Europe or the Middle East whatever the outcome would not become nuclear because of the fear of mutual destruction[22].

Counterforce strategy lowers the threshold for a nuclear war by threatening the enemy's ability to retaliate.In times of crisis each side will be frightened that the other side will be the first to launch a debilitating counterforce attack. The pressure to strike first will therefore be enormous.

Paradoxically, it is this lowering of the nuclear threshold that is thought by some to raise the credibility of nuclear deterrence and therefore our security[23]. The lowering of the nuclear threshold is also the basis of the NATO strategy of flexible response and first use of nuclear weapons[24] but in this case it has been achieved by integrating battlefield and theatre nuclear weapons with conventional forces.

Thus, to the risk of a
nuclear war by accident has been added
nuclear war by misperception (counterforce strategy) and
nuclear war by escalation (NATO flexible response).

Counterforce — an economic strategy

Another explanation for the development of a counterforce strategy, with its inherent risks, is that the US is attempting to break the Soviet economy. Although both superpowers spend approximately the same total amount on their defence, this is twice the burden for the Soviet Union because their GNP (economic wealth) is half that of the USA[9][25]. The recently publicised Pentagon document "Fiscal Year 1984-1988 Defence Guidance"[26] supports this economic argument. It asserts:

that the US and its allies should in peacetime declare economic and technological war on the Soviet Union . . . that the US should develop weapons for the Soviets to counter, impose disproportionate costs, open up new areas of major military competition and obsolesce previous Soviet investment.

This economic argument may be one of the reasons for deploying Cruise missiles. Although Cruise missiles are highly accurate, their advocates point out that they are too slow to be counterforce weapons. However because they have a small radar image (no bigger than a seagull) and fly very low they will be extremely difficult for the Soviets to detect with their present radar systems. To prevent a surprise attack the Soviets will be forced to deploy aircraft along their borders equipped with "look-down" radar at an estimated cost of over £35,000 million.[27]

Economic war is potentially dangerous and it should be remembered that the economic collapse of Germany brought about by reparations to France was one factor which facilitated Hitler's rise to power[28]. Intense economic pressure may therefore produce unpredictable effects.

Counterforce — a strategy of the military/industrial complex

Many consider that the enemy of democracy lies as much within our borders as without. President Eisenhower's warning of the power of the military-industrial complex created by the needs of World War II were well justified. There is considerable evidence to suggest that the economic and political vested interests of the military-industrial complex contributes more to the momentum of the arms race than does the threat of Soviet domination[29].

In both the USA and USSR there are less than 200 cities and towns with populations of over 150,000. The 400 pin heads on the map represent nuclear explosions on these centres resulting in the death of $\frac{1}{3}$ of the entire population of each country — more than enough for deterrence.

Effective air defence against bombers meant that Mutual Destruction was not assured.

It was the advent of ballistic missiles against which there was no defence that gave rise to the doctrine of Mutually Assured Destruction (most people's idea of deterrence). By 1961 the USA could deliver 200 warheads by ballistic missiles. By 1964 the USSR could do likewise.

1960's

The 16,000 pin heads on the map, represent random explosions of the total number of strategic (intercontinental) nuclear warheads possessed by the USA and the USSR in 1981.[23]

The SALT II Agreement of Vienna 1979 (unratified by the USA) allows the combined number of strategic nuclear warheads to increase to well over 20,000 by 1985 when the treaty expires.[19]

If as well as strategic, theatre and tactical nuclear warheads are taken into the account then the number of pin heads on the map can be doubled.[11]

The radius of the pin heads is 10 miles on the map scale. The shock wave of a 1 megaton airburst would cause extensive damage to domestic buildings 10 miles from detonation.

1980's

Deterrence Policy

Based on the threat of being able to retaliate after an attack with such devastating effect that a potential aggressor is deterred from attacking.

For deterrence to be effective, the ability to retaliate must survive the initial attack. Hence the heavy reliance on submarine-launched missiles and hardened silos for land-based missiles.

For both the USA and USSR the possession of 400-600 nuclear weapons would give each the potential to destroy $\frac{1}{3}$-$\frac{1}{2}$ of the other's population — more than sufficient for effective deterrence.

Counterforce Strategy

Based on the stringent requirement of destroying the enemy's weapons quickly, efficiently and WITHOUT WARNING.

This means a LARGE NUMBER of offensive weapons which can approach their targets without detection. It also means HIGHLY ACCURATE and reliable weapons which guarantee destroying the enemy's weapons before they can be launched.

In both the USA and USSR the patterns of technological progress over the past decade show a deliberate development of counterforce capability.

The defensive posture of each side to counterforce strategy is to have their weapons ready to be launched on warning (like a gun with the safety catch off).

As 'launch on warning' relies heavily on computers, the chance of technical failure resulting in false alarms makes an accidental war ever more likely.

Medical Effects

IMMEDIATE EFFECTS

Nuclear explosions produce heat, blast and radiation. Heat and blast give rise to burns and trauma.

Trauma:

Caused by collapse of buildings, flying debris and direct blast effects. Typical examples are shown:

Severe leg injury

Severe hand injury

Burns:

Caused by direct heat flash and indirectly by burning materials. These are often complicated by toxic smoke (which is often produced by modern furniture) and/or flame inhalation.

Child with severe body burns   Flash burns to face (Hiroshima)

These types of injuries require prompt treatment and may take weeks or months of intensive care and reconstructive surgery.

A one megaton explosion over a city would produce many thousands of such injured persons and overwhelm the medical capacity of the developed world. In the whole of the UK there are only 106 beds specifically assigned for serious burns cases[1].

# of Nuclear War

DELAYED EFFECTS

Radiation sickness:

Radioactivity kills dividing cells. This affects primarily the gut lining and the blood forming cells and can result in uncontrollable diarrhoea, vomiting, internal bleeding, massive infection, coma and death within hours, days or weeks. Survivors may never fully recover.

Infectious diseases:

Insanitary conditions from thousands of rotting corpses, flies, and vermin together with lowered resistance from radiation and malnutrition provide the best possible conditions for uncontrollable infectious diseases. These will include hepatitis, dysentry, tuberculosis, cholera, typhoid fever and typhus[30][31]. Many of these are fatal without intensive medical treatment.

A young man dying of radiation sickness.
Facial spots due to subcutaneous bleeding (Hiroshima).

Photograph: Kimura Gonichi from U.S. Army returned material courtesy of Research Institute for Nuclear Medicine and Biology Hiroshima University.

Smallpox (Glasgow 1920)

You cannot detect lethal radiation without sophisticated instruments. You will therefore not know whether you are being exposed.

In 1967 it was estimated that 10 million people suffered from smallpox of whom 2 million died.

It took 12 years of international co-operation before the World Health Organisation could declare that in 1980 Smallpox had been eradicated[32]. This achievement cost 300 million dollars, the equivalent of the cost of 2.5 days of the nuclear arms race.

LONG TERM EFFECTS

Cancer:

Increased environmental radiation will cause an increase in cancer. For example, the incidence of leukaemia increased in Japanese survivors, especially in children.

Cancer

Leukaemia

Birth Defects:

Radiation causes genetic mutations; these can result in birth defects. Following a full scale nuclear war we can expect many more abnormal babies.

Microcephaly

Malnutrition:

Our diet depends upon agriculture, trade, industry and transport. These will be largely destroyed, together with the skills inherent in their operation. Starvation will become a permanent aspect of life as it is in poorer countries[31]. Deficiency diseases such as rickets, kwashiorkor, beri-beri and scurvy are likely. Infant mortality would inevitably increase.

Infertility:

Irradiation of the reproductive organs can cause sterility.

Modern medical facilities, which are the product of centuries of development, cannot be recreated easily. The knowledge and pool of skills that we have acquired will be irretrievably lost and our resources destroyed. The only effective medical response to nuclear war is prevention.

The Wind of Change

Following a Nuclear Attack, 50% of deaths could result from fallout radiation. (BMA Report — 1983).[1]

In a Nuclear War it is likely that many victims will suffer from the combined effects of radiation, burns, and blast. Consequently, injuries which may be relatively minor under normal circumstances could be fatal when combined with others of similar severity, particularly in the absence of adequate treatment and basic sanitation.
(BMA Report — 1983)

Most Doctors and other Health Professionals would be unable to render assistance even if they themselves were unharmed because many of the casualties would be in areas of lethal fallout. (BMA Report — 1983)

Raymond Briggs

There is no effective antidote to acute radiation. Measures that might have marginal effects would not be available after a Nuclear War[35].

The explosion of a single nuclear bomb of the size used at Hiroshima over a major city in the United Kingdom is likely to produce so many cases of trauma and burns requiring hospital treatment that the remaining medical services in the United Kingdom would be completely overwhelmed. (BMA Report — 1983)

HEAT AND BLAST EFFECTS FROM A ONE MEGATON EXPLOSION ONE MILE ABOVE BATTERSEA POWER STATION (on a clear day)

Heat effects

Example of heat effects at various distances:-

Hyde Park:- (2 miles) Trees burn spontaneously; water in the Serpentine boils.

St Paul's Cathedral:- (3 miles) Car tyres ignite; sheet metal on buses ignites. Petrol in cars ignites.

Shepherd's Bush:- (4 miles) Furniture inside buildings ignites.

Kentish Town:- (4.5 miles) Human tissue charred to bone (temperature 1800°C).

Golder's Green:- (7 miles) Full thickness skin burns to those in open. Fatal.

Hendon:- (8.5 miles) Severe second degree burns; fatal if not treated.

Harrow:- (11 miles) Eyes: permanent damage to anyone looking at fireball.

Stanmore:- (12.5 miles) Severe sunburn.

			Ground Zero			
13 miles	8 miles	4.3 3 2.5 2		2 2.5 3	4.3	
Arrival of blast (seconds)				9	17	
Wind Speed (m.p.h.)				300	160	

note: at 7.4 miles wind speed is at hurricane force

26

London

Blast effects

Zone A:- Most buildings levelled; Tower blocks fall. 98% of people in this area will die as a result of heat and blast.

Zone B:- Typical houses destroyed; Damage to heavier structures; Gas mains severed.

Camden Town:- (3.75 miles) Winds of 200 mph will result in people being thrown about at 20 mph — resulting in skull fractures in more than 50%. Also common:- compound fractures and crush injuries.

Zone C:- Walls of steel frame buildings ɔwn away; severe damage to houses. Home Office Mark I Garden Shelters destroyed.

Bethnal Green:- (5.2 miles) Injuries from penetrating glass.

Zone D:- Damage to most structures as far as Biggin Hill (13 miles south); windows blown in and roof tiles dislodged.

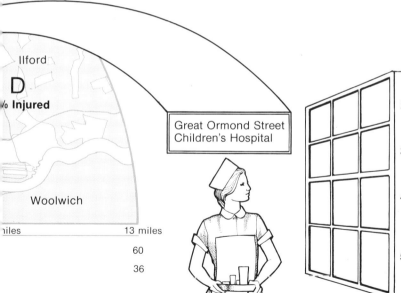

Ilford

D

% Injured

Great Ormond Street Children's Hospital

Woolwich

miles

13 miles

60

36

Experience of a nurse looking out of a window on a clear day — from Great Ormond Street Children's Hospital

1. Flash of light three miles away resulting in permanent blindness.

2. A fraction of a second later, intense heat felt on the face and bare arms resulting in third degree (full thickness) burns, with charring down to bone.

3. Fifteen seconds later, she is dazed, semi-comatose and blind. The windows are blown in resulting in severe penetrating glass injuries.

4. A fraction of a second later, she is thrown across the ward at 50 feet per second (34 mph) by the blast and is brought to an abrupt halt on the far side of the ward as her head hits the wall: her skull is fractured.

5. As this is happening, the hospital building partially collapses. The Nurse is pinned to the floor by fallen masonry, resulting in severe trauma.

Lying in State

The recently published report on the medical effects of nuclear war by the British Medical Association (BMA) Board of Science & Education states that

There are discrepancies between the projections for blast, heat and radiation produced by the Home Office and Scientists Against Nuclear Arms (SANA). The latter rely on methods and figures derived for the most part from the United States Department of Defense and the Office of Technology Assessment. We have examined the methods for calculating the projections used by SANA and the Working Party believes, on the evidence it has received, that the projections from SANA give a more realistic estimate of the blast, heat and radiation effects of nuclear weapons. We understand that the Home Office is currently revising its calculations.

The next few pages illustrate the way the Home Office have underestimated the casualties resulting from a nuclear explosion and raises the question as to whether these discrepancies are the result of incompetence or are part of a deliberate process of deception.

Burn casualties ignored:

In a nuclear explosion one-third of the energy is released as heat and consequently there will be a considerable number of burns casualties.

The current Home Office computer model for casualty predictions makes no estimate at all for burns casualties[36] [37], even though the Department of Health & Social Services (DHSS) expect "vast numbers of burns casualties"[38]. These calculations are difficult because thermal effects are dependent on weather, time of year, and number of people caught out in the open at the time of the explosion[39]. However the American Office of Technology Assessment has derived estimates of burns casualties under a variety of different conditions[40], and the same approach has been used in the Oppenshaw & Steadman computer model used by SANA[41].

Blast casualties underestimated:

There are large discrepancies between Home Office and American figures for blast casualties which are illustrated opposite.

The Home Office use casualty figures arising from CONVENTIONAL explosions while the Americans have based theirs on NUCLEAR explosions.

Following an explosion blast damage to buildings depends primarily upon two factors:-
1) The peak overpressure (measured in p.s.i.)
2) The duration of the overpressure.

In a nuclear explosion the overpressure lasts much longer (1-2 seconds) than in a conventional explosion (a few one hundredths of a second)[39]. Consequently, for the same peak overpressure a nuclear explosion will cause more destruction and loss of life than a conventional one, as was well illustrated in World War II. During the Blitz, about 70,000 tons of TNT were dropped killing approximately 60,000 people i.e. about one person killed per ton of explosive.

The two atomic bombs dropped on Japan were equivalent to 30,000 tons of TNT and killed between 100,000 and 200,000 people[10] i.e. about three to six people killed per ton of explosive (TNT equivalent).

The Home Office estimates for blast casualties in a nuclear explosion use figures arising from conventional explosions in World War II[42]. In contrast, the US Office of Technology Assessment (OTA), obtained their estimates, which they consider conservative, from data based on the Japanese experience and the atmospheric testing of nuclear weapons before the Partial Test Ban Treaty of 1963.

Blast ranges:

Blast Range is the distance from a nuclear explosion subjected to a given peak overpressure. The Home Office, in their computer model use U.S. data from Glasstone and Dolan (The Effects of Nuclear Weapons)[37].

In Home Office publications there are errors and inconsistencies for quoted blast ranges [43] [44]. These errors all result in the blast damage areas being smaller than they should be; for air bursts they have reduced blast damage areas by as much as 40%. (Page 60 ref. 1).

In addition, the "Weapon Effects Calculators" issued by the Home Office to Scientific Advisers have built-in errors. This results in the blast ranges, for higher overpressures, being smaller than those given in Glasstone and Dolan — as shown in the illustration opposite.

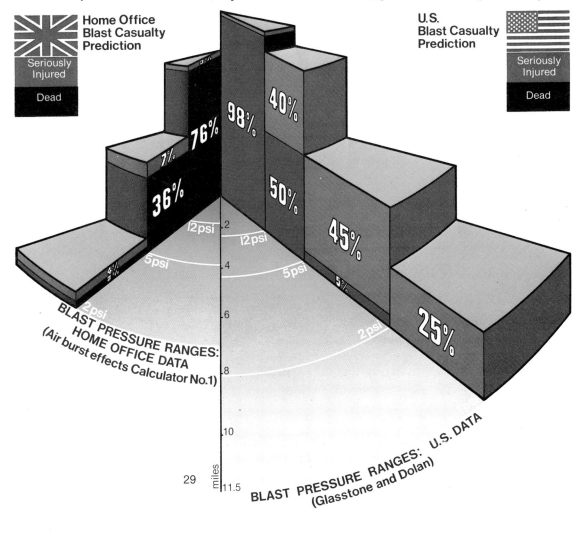

Discrepancies in Blast Casualty Predictions for a 1 Megaton Air Burst (7800 feet)

Home Office Blast Casualty Prediction — Seriously Injured / Dead

U.S. Blast Casualty Prediction — Seriously Injured / Dead

BLAST PRESSURE RANGES: HOME OFFICE DATA (Air burst effects Calculator No.1)

BLAST PRESSURE RANGES: U.S. DATA (Glasstone and Dolan)

29

Fallout casualties underestimated

The Home Office has underestimated casualties from fallout by overestimating the protective factor of buildings, ignoring the effect of blast damage and by underestimating the lethality of radiation.

Misleading protective factors

The protection that an individual has against fallout radiation will depend on the thickness and density of material between that individual and the radiation source, and is known as the PROTECTIVE FACTOR (PF). This is the ratio between the radiation outside the building or shelter and the radiation that penetrates inside. The higher the value the greater protection from radiation. For example PF2 means that only half (½) of the radiation penetrates, while PF10 means that only one tenth (1/10) of the radiation penetrates.

> This illustration shows the effect of a 1 megaton air burst (7800 ft) followed by a blanket of fallout radiation (2,500 rads) from a nearby ground burst — a situation that occurred in many places in the 1980 Square Leg Exercise.[46] [47]
> (Burn casualties have not been taken into account.)
> The blast zone reaching out to 1 psi covers an area of 415 square miles. Assuming the average UK density of 593 persons per square mile, the area would encompass ¼ of a million people or 1½ million people if it were central London.

The US Office of Technology Assessment (OTA) quote a variety of studies on Protection Factors assumed for houses and shelters in the USA[40]. For estimating fallout casualties a range of values has been used:

PF3   for the entire population assuming that no civil defence measures have been used.

PF5-6   for people remaining in their homes.

PF10-40 for people with access to proper fallout shelters.

The OTA estimate that on average the PFs would be in the range of 5 to 6. By contrast the Home Office have assigned a very high average PF of over 20 to British housing stock[45]. The very high PFs used by the Home Office for ordinary houses are based on dubious assumptions[46], one of which is that the entire population would be able to carry out the measures suggested in the HMSO civil defence pamphlet "Protect and Survive". Such measures include:

1) Bricking up windows and doors;
2) Blocking off fireplaces with sand bags;
3) Building an inner refuge.

The net result is that the Home Office estimates for fallout casualties are misleadingly low.

CASUALTIES BASED ON HOME OFFICE ASSUMPTIONS (= 1% of people in blast zone)

Blast damage ignored

Blast damage to houses reduces protection from fallout radiation. Even light blast damage such as missing roof tiles or broken windows and doors allows radioactive dust to be blown into the house greatly reducing its PF value.

The Home Office Square Leg exercise envisaged over 205 megatons being dropped on military and city targets of which about 100 megatons would be ground bursts creating local radioactive fallout[47]. Oppenshaw and Steadman calculated that in this exercise most inhabited parts of Britain experienced a blast overpressure greater than 1 psi which would break most of the windows in the country![48] Although no bomb was dropped on the centre of London in the "Square Leg" exercise, Green *et al* found that 75% of the GLC area was subjected to overpressures greater than 2 psi[46]. The Home Office estimates that the "Type I improvised garden shelter" would collapse under a peak overpressure greater than 1.5psi[44], so in most of London these shelters would be demolished before they could serve their intended function as fallout shelters.

Oppenshaw and Steadman using their computer model on the "Square Leg" exercise were able to estimate FALLOUT casualty figures which were dependent on the national PF value used:

PF1 (no protection)   22.5 million casualties
PF5   10.5 million casualties
PF20   3.5 million casualties

Descriptions of the Home Office computer calculations make no reference to the effect of blast damage on PF values and it appears that this relationship is ignored[36][37]. This is illustrated by the Home Office casualty prediction of less than one million deaths for a nuclear attack, similar to the Square Leg exercise, involving 193 megatons on military and city targets of which 109 megatons were ground bursts producing the local fallout[36]. To obtain this mortality rate they must have used a PF greater than 20 which is the PF for undamaged houses.

The American figures indicate that more realistic PFs would be between 3 and 6. This would result in 8 to 10 million deaths from fallout and is a far cry from the Home Office estimate of "under 1 million".

PF 1 (2500 rads)   PF 2 (1250 rads)   PF 4 (625 rads)   PF 6 (416 rads)

DEAD

SERIOUSLY INJURED

SURVIVORS

Blast
Radiation

CASUALTIES BASED ON US DATA (= 1% of people in blast zone)

Lethality of radiation underestimated

The Home Office have also underestimated casualties by mis-application of data concerning the lethality of radiation.

Definitions: Unit of radiation = rad
LD50 = lethal dose for 50% of people
LD50 for healthy adults = 450 rads

Thus if a group of 100 healthy adults are exposed to 450 rads over a short period of time (less than one day), 50 will die even with intensive hospital treatment. (See box) The LD50 is less for children (with their smaller bodies) and old people.

Operational evaluation dose (OED)

In order to calculate operational radiation exposure limits for civil defence workers the Home Office use a formula to calculate "OED" which incorporates two pieces of data[43]:
1) Healthy adults exposed to less than 150 rads will show few if any signs of radiation exposure;
2) The body can repair about 10 rads of radiation damage per day.

The formula for "OED" is:

$$OED = \text{total radiation doses} - 150 - (10t)$$
(where t = number of days after exposure)

Medical significance of OED values

Total Dose	Symptoms/effects	OED (t=0)
0 rads	none	−150
150 rads	nausea and 'feeling ill'	0
200 rads	vomiting	+50
250 rads	diarrhoea	+100
450 rads	50% of healthy adults die (LD 50)	+300
600 rads	chances of survival limited	+450
800 rads	90 to 100% of healthy adults die	+650

First misapplication of OED by Home Office

When it comes to calculating civilian fallout casualties the Home Office quote the LD 50 as 450 rads, in agreement with other sources. However it has recently been revealed that the Home Office in their computer model DO NOT USE 450 rads AS THE LD50; instead they equate the LD50 with an OED value of 450 which represents a dose of 600 rads i.e. 150 rads greater than the LD50[37]. This appears to be a fraudulent application of the OED expression.

Second misapplication of the OED by the Home Office

At the request of the Home Office the Protection Against Ionising Radiation Committee reassessed the effects of radiation exposure. Their informal advice to the Home Office suggested that humans are much more resistant to radiation exposure than had previously been thought. This advice, which the Home Office accepted, was:

1) The threshold below which no ill effects from radiation are expected should be increased from 150 to 200 rads.
2) That the amount of radiation that the body can repair per day should be increased from 10 to 15 rads.
3) That the LD50, the dose at which 50% of people are expected to die, should be increased from 450 to 600 rads.

The basis for this advice has not been published. (Page 84 ref. 1). Using these new figures the final row of the table opposite becomes:

Total dose		OED
600 rads	chances of survival limited	+400
800 rads	90 to 100% of healthy adults die	+600

From this it is clear that an LD50 of 600 rads is equivalent to an OED value of 400. However the Home Office again misapply the LD50 and equate it with an OED value of 600 which is equivalent to a dose of 800 rads.

Radiation Dose – Short Exposure To Whole Body

ESTIMATES OF 50% LETHAL DOSE

SYMPTOMS

OED
Values at time of dose
(ie t=O)

OLD FORMULA   NEW FORMULA

Survival Impossible   Central nervous system affected:
Lethargy, unsteadiness, convulsions, coma, and death within days.

1000 rads → 850   800

New Home Office value

800 rads   800 rads → 650   600

Survival Improbable   Gut affected:
Day 1: Generally unwell, nausea and vomiting.
Weeks 1-2: Fever, profuse bloody diarrhoea.
Week 3: If still alive, bone-marrow affected.

Old Home Office value

600 rads   600 rads → 450   400

Accepted value *

450 rads   450 rads →   50% mortality (LD 50) for young fit adults.   300   250

*
1	National Radiological Protection Board (1979) pp 43-44.[60]	350-500 rads
2	Home Office advice to scientific advisers: Table E10.[61]	450 rads
3	Home Office (1974) Nuclear Weapons (HMSO, London) p 11.[43]	340-530 rads
4	Glastone and Dolan (1977) table 12.108 pp 580-581.[39]	450 rads
5	Rotblat (1981) Figure 7 p 35.[35]	330 rads

Survival Probable   Bone-marrow affected:
Days 1-2: Generally unwell, nausea and vomiting.
Weeks 2-3: Fever, skin haemorrhages, mouth ulcers, loss of hair with more than 300 rads.
Day 30: Maximum bone marrow suppression, lowered resistance to disease.

300 rads → 150   100

150 rads → 0   —50

Survival certain
Either no symptoms or generally unwell and nausea.
Fall in blood lymphocyte count.

0 rads → —150   —200

Square Leg

"Square Leg" was the name given to the 1980 Home Defence exercise. The envisaged attack was 131 warheads (62 air bursts and 69 ground bursts) totalling 205 megatons on a mixture of military and city targets.

1979 Population of Britain: 54 million (each figure = 1 million)

Predicted Casualties based on

Home Office assumption ——————————————— Openshaw/Steadman assumption

Deaths from —— Burns / Blast / Radiation

Seriously injured

Survivors

Square Leg

After several weeks of mounting tension, war was declared. Four days later, on Thursday 19th September 1980 at 11.55 a.m. 'Attack Warning Red' was given. Nine minutes later the first wave of bombs fell on Britain hitting strategic and industrial targets. Square Leg, the 1980 Civil Defence exercise, was in full swing[47]. Three hours after the initial attack a second wave of bombs arrived hitting targets of which many were cities. For some reason London itself was not a target although it would have suffered considerable damage from bombs that landed on the outskirts[46].

Targets chosen in the exercise seemed realistic in that many of them, though relatively unknown, were strategically important. Such targets included the two electronic listening posts at Chicksands (USAF) and RAF Digby; the two very low frequency radio stations at Rugby and Criggon, used for communicating with submerged submarines; and the US underwater monitoring post at Brawdy.

A large proportion of the strategic targets in the exercise were US bases which is not surprising as there are over one hundred such bases in Britain[63]. The official figure given for the number of US bases in Britain is 56. However, this figure was only arrived at after a series of parliamentary questions which began with the admission of 12 bases plus a 'few other facilities'[64]. When the 'few other facilities' were listed, the figure rose to 53[65]; and then to 56 when asked if the list was complete[66].

There were two noteable features of the attack. The first was underwater explosions in the Thames and Clyde estuaries producing tidal waves which would have flooded London and Glasgow. The other feature was the attack on four nuclear reactors at Dungeness and Dounreay and the nuclear waste reprocessing plant, Windscale (renamed Sellafield). The destruction of these nuclear installations, particularly Windscale, would have resulted in the release of large amounts of long lived radioactive material, increasing considerably not only the area of lethal radioactive fallout but also the time taken for the fallout to decay[62].

Planning to Survive

When contemplating the consequences of a nuclear attack on Britain one can, perhaps, forgive civil defence planners for thinking in terms of an evolutionary bottleneck from which only the 'fittest' will survive. Certainly this is the flavour of the North East Thames Health Authority War Plan which states:

If all the trees and much of the brushwood are felled, a forest may not regenerate for centuries. If a sufficient number of the great trees is left, however, if felling is to some extent selective and controlled, recovery is swift. In its way, a nation is like a forest and the aim of war planning is to secure the survival of the great trees . . . there will remain brushwood enough, if thirty million survivors can be so described. The planning policy is clearly elitist and is so because no wider policy is possible.

The appendix to this War Plan lists major historical disasters, from the plague of Justinian in AD 540 to Hulegu Khan invading Mesopotamia in 1258, in which the survival of leaders determined the survival of nations. The list is followed by the observation that:

We have warning now of the modern equivalent of plague. That is why isolation points (bunkers) *have already been equipped.*

In the background notes to the 1980 Square Leg exercise, Her Majesty's Government requested that the nation's art treasures be moved to places of safety. Two days before the expected attack the 'great trees' also moved to their bunkers.

Hard Luck, Hard Rock

Considerable public alarm arose when details of the 1980 civil defence exercise Square Leg were published in the *New Statesman*[47]. In general, the sheer scale of a nuclear attack on Britain envisaged by the Home Office, had not been appreciated.
Anticipating the inevitable publicity both the Home Office and SANA presented target plans for the 1982 civil defence exercise with code names of Hard Rock and Hard Luck respectively.

Predicted Casualties based on

Hard Rock

Hard Rock was to be the largest civil defence exercise since 1958, but was cancelled because one third of the Local Authorities refused to take part. In the past the Home Office have stressed that target plans for civil defence exercises "should not be taken as realistic descriptions . . . of the weight or distribution of an enemy's attack":[38] Hard Rock seems to be a case in point.

The attack (54 bombs with a total of 48 megatons) was puny compared with previous exercises such as Square Leg (131 bombs; with a total of 205 megatons). In addition, contrary to the recent technological advances in delivering nuclear warheads with a high degree of accuracy (500 metres and less), over half the bombs in the planned exercise missed their intended targets by 6 to 10 miles. Fortunately, most of those targets missed were cities. Some targets that did receive direct hits such as the top of Mount Carneddau had no military, industrial or civilian significance as far as we know.[38]

Hard Luck

The attack constructed by SANA was based on known Soviet Eurostrategic weapons. Those weapons, thought to be aimed at Britain, were assigned actual targets[52].

The targets selected were principally military and strategic ones, with a few urban areas included because of their industrial significance.

The attack (362 bombs with an average yield of 0.6 Mt — making a total of 222 megatons) can be seen as limited in two senses:

1) Major population centres were not deliberately targeted for their own sake.
2) Since the Soviets already possess significant weapons to direct more than 600 megatons on such an important target as the UK, the attack did not employ all the weapons that would be available.

It is interesting that the principal criticism of Hard Luck by the Home Office was that an attack of 222 megatons was excessively large, when they themselves used 205 megatons in Square Leg (1980), and indeed, have considered "worst case" scenarios involving 500 and 3000 megatons[36].

Lying in state: Post Mortem

It is difficult to conclude that errors in the Home Office casualty model when taken together are not a deliberate attempt to minimise the perceived consequences of a nuclear attack.

Although the reasons for these discrepancies are known only to those who constructed the model (members of the Home Office F6 Division), we suggest a possible motive.

The development of nuclear ballistic missiles by both the United States and the Soviet Union brought about the realisation that little could be done to protect civilian populations from the effects of a nuclear attack. Consequently, in 1968 civil defence plans in Britain were shelved. The decision was in keeping with the current idea that since both sides knew that they would be destroyed in a nuclear war, the possession of nuclear weapons guaranteed the peace.

However, with the deployment of new counterforce weapons, the risk of nuclear war has been increasing (pp 16-17).

It is, perhaps, in recognition of these changes in nuclear strategy that the Home Office have revived civil defence planning.

Certainly, the most recent civil defence exercises reflect the changes away from purely civilian targets to civilian/military ones (see table). The inclusion of military targets greatly increases the weight of attack.

Civil Defence Exercises	Number of Bombs	Total Megatons	Target
Plans for MAD strategy:			
Dutch Treat 1957	8	8	Cities
Exercise 1960	15	56	Cities
Changes to plans for counterforce strategy:			
Inside right 1976	?	?	?
Scrum half 1978	130	200	Military/Civilian
Square Leg 1980	131	205	Military/Civilian
Adverse publicity			
Hard Rock 1982	54	48	Military/Civilian

As was appreciated in the 60's, little can be done to protect civilian populations from the effects of nuclear attack. Home Office plans, therefore, concentrate on the survival of some form of regional authority (by means of shelter in deep bunkers) to be ready to organise the survivors in the post-holocaust Britain. Because of this, for the purpose of civil defence planning, casualty predictions are irrelevant, although they do have considerable impact on the public's opinion with regard to Britain's nuclear defence policies. So Home Office figures which give an optimistic impression of the consequences of a nuclear attack are useful in terms of manipulating public feeling.

A Home Office circular (E53/73) suggests that for planning purposes in the event of a nuclear attack, a survival rate of 60% can be assumed for the worst affected areas and 95% survival in other areas.

In another example quoted by Duncan Campbell[38], Sir Leslie Mavor and other Home Office staff presented a paper at a NATO conference in 1977, entitled "Post Strike Scene: UK". This paper gives, after a 180 megaton attack, an immediate survival rate of between 75-85 per cent; but after a year the survival rate dropped to between 30 and 50 percent.

In 1980 Lord Belstead used these figures in a public speech. Now the 75 per cent survival figure has stuck in people's minds, as it is often quoted by government home defence lobbyists as well as being used for local authority planning purposes.

The obsessive secrecy by the Home Office about civil defence matters has allowed the basis upon which they predict casualty figures to go unchallenged for some considerable time. This secrecy in the long run, is counter productive as it encourages a loss of confidence in the process of government as a whole.

The main cricitism of civil defence in a nuclear age is that it distracts attention away from the real problem of how do we prevent a nuclear war from ever happening.

European Security

The SS20 and Pershing II are both ballistic missiles with nuclear warheads; part of their flight goes outside the earth's atmosphere. By contrast, the Cruise Missile (Ground Launched Cruise Missile — G.L.C.M.) is effectively a pilotless aircraft with a (nuclear) warhead. Although it flies at a sub-sonic speed it is difficult to detect — partly because it flies very low over the earth's surface.

During the 1960's intermediate and short range missiles were deployed within Europe. The Soviet Union's missiles were mainly land-based (e.g. SS4 & SS5). The West relied more on submarine systems (e.g. Polaris) and less on the ground-based systems such as the Pershing 1.

In 1976 the USSR began to deploy the SS20, a semi-mobile missile with three warheads and a range of 5000 kilometres. This missile was eventually to replace the SS4 & SS5 which being slow to launch from fixed sites had become vulnerable to American missiles[53]. By Easter, 1983, 351 SS20's had been deployed although two-thirds of these are thought to be assigned for Europe. However, according to the Pentagon, the balance of European forces was:

WEST		EAST	
Delivery System	Warheads	Delivery System	Warheads
0	0	SS20 351	1053

Hence President Reagan's call for a Zero Option; in this, the Soviet Union was asked to remove all her SS20's and in return the USA would not deploy any Pershing II or Cruise Missiles in Europe. But, as stated above, the West has relied on other, non land-based, systems. If these other systems are brought in, the balance looks different

WEST		EAST	
Delivery System	Warheads	Delivery System	Warheads
2236	3398	3429	4161

for breakdown of figures, see table, page 40

Even these figures do not take into account all the nuclear weapons assigned for use in the European theatre such as artillery shells, mines and depth charges. If all these were included in the balance, the West would have approximately 8000 nuclear devices and the East over 4161[67].

The situation is complicated by the fact that long range, intercontinental-missiles of both superpowers could be targeted on Europe — and probably are. (See**, page 40). In any event, both East and West have the ability to completely devastate each other whatever the arguments may be regarding the total number of warheads. Effective parity already exists; for if a country can be destroyed once, then the ability to destroy it several times over becomes irrelevant.

The debate regarding the deployment of Cruise and Pershing II is complex; but as argued above, effective parity already exists.
What, then, is the purpose of these new weapons?

Nuclear weapons assigned specifically for Europe (long and medium range systems)

WEST		Warheads	EAST	Warheads
1. Land-based missiles				
Pershing 1A	(USA & FRG)	180	SS-4 & SS-5*	180
SSBS S3	(France)	18	SS-20*	648
			SS-11 & SS-19**	480
		198		1308
2. Submarine-based missiles				
Poseidon C3***	(USA)	400	SS-N-5	43
Polaris A3****	(UK)	192		
MSBS-M20	(France)	80		
		672		43
3. Nuclear capable aircraft				
FN-111 etc	(USA)	1036	Tu-16 Badger	498
Vulcan/Buccaneer/Jag.	(UK)	362	Tu-22 Blinder	150
Mirage 1VA/111/Jag./			Tu-22M Backfire	150
S.Etendard	(France)	277	Su-24/Mig-23/27/17/20	1812
F-104 etc	(Rest of NATO)	853	Mig-23 (Rest of WTO)	200
		2528		2810
TOTAL		3398		4161

Sources: SIPRI 82 & 83; IISS 1982-1983. (These figures represent the averages from these
two sources.)

    *SS-4/5 & SS-20 figures represent 2/3 of the total USSR force for these weapons.
   **The SS-11 & SS-19 are strategic missiles (ICBMs) some of which are thought
    to be targeted on Europe[68].
  ***Poseidon C3 — only the 5 submarines allocated to SACEUR included; the war-
    head figure is sometimes given as 800.
 ****Polaris A3 — 3 warheads per missile (Chevaline figures not quoted).

The following points may help clarify the discussion:

1. While the SS20, Pershing II and Cruise can all be regarded as long range theatre nuclear weapons, their significance is entirely different by reasons of geography. The SS20 threatens Western Europe but not the USA and therefore cannot be regarded as a strategic weapon. However, the Pershing II and GLCM threaten both Eastern Europe and the Soviet Union and are, threfore, effectively strategic weapons.

2. The NATO decision to deploy Pershing II and Cruise Missiles was based on military considerations — i.e. to have the option to strike at military targets in Eastern Europe or the Soviet Union. It was not primarily a response to the SS20 though this was used politically as the reason:

3. The SS20 is not particularly accurate (CEP 750 metres) . However, both the Pershing II and Cruise are exceptionally accurate (CEP 40/50 metres) and so, unlike the SS20, have the ability to destroy hardened military targets. The Pershing II .is particularly suited for destroying "time urgent" targets such as command, control and communication bunkers[55].

4. The Pershing II and Cruise are both ground launched systems and both have a limited range. They were clearly not, therefore, intended for deployment within America. Since development of both these systems started in the 1970's it seems reasonable to assume that the US Military envisaged a role for them in Europe.

5. De Gaulle did not believe in the so-called nuclear umbrella of the USA protecting Europe. He had argued that no US President would sacrifice Chicago for Paris. Since that time, many politicians and others have come to share De Gaulle's view.
    The firing of Pershing II and Cruise from Western Europe eastwards might be construed as an act for which the USA was

responsible. The Soviet Union might be expected to answer with an attack on the United States mainland — and has said as much[56]. It would therefore seem that De Gaulle's argument still holds for Pershing II and Cruise; the firing of these weapons in defence of Europe would be suicide for the United States and so can barely be credible.

What, then, is the intention of the USA in agreeing to deploy these new missiles on European soil?
There are at least two possible answers to this question:
   A. The missiles may be intended for use against targets confined to Eastern Europe with the hope that the ensuing nuclear war would be limited to Europe leaving both superpowers intact.

   B. The missiles could be intended for military targets within the Soviet Union as part of a Counterforce plan involving US strategic weapons which would include their 3780 air-launched Cruise missiles, some of which have already been deployed.

In this latter context, the deployment of Pershing II and Cruise could be seen as an integral part of Presidential Directive 59 (of July '80) in which President Carter formally adopted the counterforce strategy, first considered by President Eisenhower's Secretary of State, Dulles, in 1957 and further implemented by the then US Defense Secretary Schlesinger in the 1970's[55].

6. All Arms Limitation Agreements to date have depended upon the ability of both superpowers to verify the agreement. This has become possible with satellite surveillance. Many analysts fear that the deployment of Cruise would be the end of verification because these missiles are not only physically small and so easy to hide, but, unlike other nuclear delivery systems, they are relatively cheap and therefore suitable as conventional weapons. This makes them ambiguous — for it is not possible to tell whether a warhead is conventional or nuclear from satellite pictures.

Conclusion:-

These highly accurate weapon systems are designed for fighting a nuclear war; in particular, Pershing II has the ability to destroy the other side's military installations a short time after firing. Hence, even if a "Launch on Warning" policy is not at present technically feasible, in times of crisis there would inevitably be great pressures on both sides to fire their weapons first — for to wait could result in one's own missiles being destroyed. This inevitably leads to the conclusion that the deployment of Pershing II and Cruise missiles will reduce European security by making nuclear war more, and not less, likely.

Possibilities for reducing tension:-

The USSR has repeatedly said that it would not be the first to use nuclear weapons. Field Marshal Lord Carver and others have recently advocated that NATO should also adopt such a "No First Strike" policy[57]. It is not clear whether this would necessarily involve extra expenditure on conventional forces but, even if it did, there is good evidence to suggest that such a policy would raise the nuclear threshold and so reduce the risk of nuclear war.

The arms race over the last 30 years has followed a predictable pattern. The deployment of any new system by one superpower has resulted in the other superpower subsequently deploying a comparable or more advanced system — without either side becoming more secure. This would seem to be the inevitable result of Pershing II and Cruise being deployed.

A total freeze on the deployment of all nuclear weapon systems would overcome this danger — and at the same time remove the notion that the United States will only negotiate from a position of strength; an unrealistic proposition as it implies that the Soviet Union would agree to negotiate from an inferior position.

A recent paper[69] (TTAPS report) in the journal *Science* describes a hitherto unsuspected phenomenon which has now been called the Nuclear Winter.

In the aftermath of a nuclear war, there would be so much dust and soot injected into the atmosphere of the Northern Hemisphere that the sun would be obscured for several weeks. As the initial gloom deepened so the temperature on land would fall, such that conditions would become like an Arctic winter with sub-freezing temperatures, icy winds and perpetual darkness.

Previous studies on the global impact of Nuclear War had not predicted the phenomenon of a Nuclear Winter, partly because they underestimated the effect of dust created by nuclear explosions, but primarily because they overlooked the dramatic consequences of sooty smoke arising from massive fires.

The first to draw attention to the effects of sooty smoke were Crutzen and Birks in 1982[34]. This stimulated a number of scientists to re-examine the climatic effects of a nuclear war[70; 71].

Nuclear Dust:

Ground burst nuclear explosions inject very fine dust particles into the atmosphere. These particles have a cooling effect on the climate by scattering sunlight away from the earth's surface. The dust from megaton explosions has a far greater climatic impact than dust from smaller explosions. A megaton explosion injects dust high into the atmosphere, the stratosphere, where it is above the elements of weather (wind and rain) and so has a relatively long residence time of months to years in which to exert a climatic influence. By contrast most of the dust from nuclear explosions of less than a megaton remains in the lower part of the atmosphere (troposphere) where it is rapidly rained out within weeks.

Sooty Smoke:

About one third of the energy from a nuclear explosion is released as heat which from an air burst explosion will ignite combustible material over a large area. Most of the smoke particles from fires will be confined to the troposphere and so will be rained out within weeks. However, some smoke particles may have a longer residence time by being pumped into the stratosphere by fire storms. Sooty smoke absorbs rather than scatters light and is much more effective than dust in blotting out sunlight. In addition, although opaque to visible light, sooty smoke will be relatively transparent to infra-red radiation. So beneath the clouds of sooty smoke the ground — shadowed from the sunlight — will rapidly cool losing heat by infra-red radiation. In the short term sooty smoke will have a far greater climatic impact than dust in the stratosphere.

Predicted effects:

In the TTAPS report a wide range of nuclear war scenarios were considered ranging from a 100 Mt attack on cities to a full scale exchange of 10,000 Mt representing two thirds of the superpowers combined arsenal.

Their base line model was a 5000 Mt exchange involving 10,400 explosions (yields 0.1 to 10 Mts) distributed throughout the northern latitudes. After the first week, mainly as the result of sooty smoke, light would be reduced to about 3% of normal. A month later, when a large proportion of the smoke would be rained out — so that dust in the upper atmosphere begins to dominate the optical effects — daylight would still be only half strength. Six months after the event daylight would be 80% of normal with full recovery occurring after a year or two, by which time most of the dust in stratosphere would have drifted back to the earth's surface.

Winter

Temperatures in the northern hemisphere were predicted to drop to a mimimum three weeks after the event, possibly as low as —23°C in continental interiors. However, such extremely low temperatures would be unlikely to occur in coastal zones as a result of the huge thermal capacity of the oceans.

The subfreezing temperatures would persist for several months. After one year the temperature would still be 4°C below average because of stratospheric dust. This would be climatically very significant.

Surprisingly the computer model predicted that the 100 Mt attack on cities (1000×0.1 Mt air burst explosions) would initially produce a nuclear winter with a similar temperature drop as in the base line 5,000 Mt exchange. The reason for this was that huge amounts of smoke would arise from the burning of urban centres. However, in the absence of stratospheric dust from high yield ground burst explosions the temperatures would recover after three weeks.

A significant proportion of strategic targets are near urban centres.

Other effects:

1. The absorption of sunlight by clouds of sooty smoke will heat up the atmosphere above it. This could result in new atmospheric circulation patterns so that debris from a nuclear war in the northern hemisphere would spread and affect the southern hemisphere. This kind of effect has been observed on Mars where dust storms in one hemisphere — by heating up the atmosphere — intensify and spread to both hemispheres in a matter of days.

2. The massive fires would release large amounts of poisonous gases (carbon monoxide and hydrogen cyanide) as well as hundreds of tons of extremely persistent and toxic compounds such as dioxans and furans.

3. The amount of harmful ultra-violet radiation reaching the earth's surface in the base line 5,000 Mt exchange would be 50% greater than normal for at least a year.

4. Radioactive fallout may be more intense and widespread than expected. Previous studies had ignored the radioactive debris in the troposphere from low yield explosions which will be rained down within weeks rather than years.

The authors of the TTAPS report point out that because of uncertainties in the data and inadequacies of atmospheric modelling their predictions are necessarily imprecise. Nevertheless, they stress that because the magnitude of the effects are so large what is significant is not that they are precisely wrong but that they are approximately right.

Biological consequences:

In an accompanying paper[72] to the TTAPS report 40 scientists consider the biological consequences of a nuclear winter. Their conclusions were that the below-freezing temperatures, darkness and high doses of ionizing and ultra-violet radiation extending for many months after a large scale nuclear war would destroy the biological basis for civilisation, at least in the Northern Hemisphere. If the Southern Hemisphere were also affected there could be a global disruption of life.

The 100 Mt scenario above represents less than 0.5% of the world's megatonnage. If this "limited" amount can create a nuclear winter, what can the threatened purpose be of the remaining 99.5%? Indeed, it would appear that the counterforce strategy is now incredible and MAD; but at a much higher and more dangerous level than the MAD strategy of the 1960's.

Perceptions and Morality

The extermination of Jews by the Nazi Regime still causes public outrage. Yet we seem to be blinded by the fact that the use of nuclear weapons would result in the same kind of extermination of civilian populations. One reason for this is that during the 1950's when the doctrine of Mutually Assured Destruction was evolving, few thought about the morality of these policies as they understood and believed that nuclear deterrence would not fail, and so the question of annihilating millions was not seriously considered. But this question can no longer be dismissed since the new "crisis unstable" weapons are threatening the stability which was thought to ensue from a nuclear deterrent. (See pp 12-21)

One of the main stumbling blocks in attempting to reverse the Arms Race is the ingrained attitude that each side has of the other. Both sides perceive themselves as "peacemakers" and regard their own weapons as "good" and essential — solely for defence. The other side's weapons are perceived as bad, threatening, and excessive for purely defensive requirements.[1]

In order to justify the possession and threatened use of nuclear weapons, it becomes necessary to perceive the enemy as totally bad or evil. As the Physicist P. M. S. Blacket said some years ago:

Once a nation bases its security on an absolute weapon, such as the Atom Bomb, it becomes psychologically necessary to believe in an absolute enemy.[58]

This may well be at a subconscious level. Clearly, no nation can be absolutely evil.

Britain's nuclear deterrence can only be regarded as credible if it is assumed that in the last resort it would be used. Therefore, to accept such a policy is to accept a situation in which, if all else fails, our Government, on our behalf, would be responsible for annihilating tens of millions of Soviet Citizens — and destroying Europe in the aftermath. Such a policy would appear to be both irrational and morally unjustifiable.

The Individual's Response

The political apathy of people in time of peace indicates that they will readily allow themselves to be led to slaughter later. Because today they lack even the courage to give their signature in support of disarmament, they will be compelled to shed their blood tomorrow.

Albert Einstein.

The hopes and aspirations of human beings throughout the world are in many respects very similar, but these are becoming overshadowed by the threat of nuclear annihilation. Our feeling of helplessness caused by this can easily result in us ignoring the problem; but this will lead to catastrophe as Einstein warns. If, however, we critically study the causes and likely effects of the nuclear arms race we can, within a fairly short space of time, become more knowledgeable than many politicians in this matter. This knowledge may lead us to realise that many, while claiming to advocate disarmament, are set on an unprecedented escalation of the arms race as a result of ignorance or misinformation — particularly regarding Soviet nuclear capabilities.

As individuals in the West, where we can express our views relatively freely, we have a great responsibility to challenge the present policies which appear to be inappropriate and exceedingly dangerous. These issues are too crucial to be left to possibly ill-informed politicians.

I like to believe that people in the long run are going to do more to promote peace than governments. Indeed, I think that people want peace so much that one of these days governments had better get out of their way and let them have it.

Dwight Eisenhower (1959).

Conclusion: The Earth: Our Environment

The future of humanity can seldom have looked so uncertain as it does today. The worldwide process of industrialisation has accelerated rapidly since 1945, resulting in pollution of the atmosphere and in the loss of vast areas of the world's forests. The long-term consequences of these processes are both unpredictable and possibly irreversible, and may in the 21st century radically alter life on earth.

Since the Second World War most Third World countries have achieved their independence, but now find themselves pawns within both the world economy and the military machinations of one or other superpower.[8] (The Brandt Commission Report of 1980 warned of the destabilising effects of the poor countries getting progressively poorer, yet this report has been largely ignored.)

Compounding all these problems is the threat of nuclear annihilation. Politicians often defend present nuclear policies by emphasising the 39 years of peace Europe has enjoyed since 1945 when the first Atom Bomb was exploded. Yet 39 years is a very short time in human history. If the nuclear policies of the last decade have been appropriate, the added arsenals of nuclear weapons should have made the world a safer place now compared with the 1970s; however, most Europeans feel less secure.

The continuation of the arms race by the nuclear powers has broken the spirit if not the letter of Article VI of the Non-Proliferation Treaty.[74] As a consequence, non-nuclear weapon states may no longer feel bound by the Treaty and so develop nuclear weapons of their own: if Britain feels it is rational to base her security on a nuclear deterrent, then other countries may use the same rationale. Few analysts, however, feel that world security would be increased by such horizontal proliferation of nuclear weapons.

In December 1982, the United Nations General Assembly voted by a large majority in favour of various disarmament resolutions including one on a freeze of the deployment of all nuclear weapons. The USA and Britain voted against the freeze proposal,[59] yet had this resolution been adopted by the superpowers it could have been a first major step towards reducing East-West tension.

In the long run, progress in disarmament may only come about when individual nations accept the majority view of the United Nations on such issues. In this way, the democratic decisions of the UN will perhaps have to overrule concepts of national self-interest if humanity is to survive.

These problems facing humankind are not insoluble but their solution may require a change in the very way we think. As Martin Luther King said in another context: "We must either learn to live together as brothers or we are going to perish together as fools."

45

It has been a feature of the many failed attempts to reduce the numbers of nuclear weapons that one side puts forward a rigid take-it-or-leave-it proposal which the other side receives with extreme caution. The fact that Side A proposes something is taken as sufficient evidence that it must be to the disadvantage of Side B.

It is reasonable to suppose that the difficulty in reaching agreement will be in proportion to the magnitudes at stake. It would therefore be harder to agree to a large cut than to a series of more modest steps.

The problem of matching one weapon system with another can lead to endless argument. Complications arise from the number of warheads, the mobility of launchers, the hardness of silos, and the accuracy of guidance. These matters would be difficult to resolve in a friendly discussion between the services of one power. But in the debate between rival super-powers it is safe to assume that the problem is quite intractable.

One could conclude that a successful scheme should proceed by small steps, that it should convince both sides that each has bettered the other and, most importantly, that it should not become embroiled in the difficulties of weapon comparison.

It has proved possible to design a mechanism which has these three characteristics. Indeed it can turn to advantage the inevitable differences of opinion about weapons of the two sides.

Cutting

The plan would work as follows. Each side begins by assigning a percentage value to each nuclear device in its armoury. This percentage value represents the usefulness of the weapon to the owner. For example if the Soviet Union decided that the 350 SS-20 missiles represented, say, 15% of its nuclear strength then the military value of each missile would be 0.04292%. The total percentage value of nuclear devices on one side must by definition come to 100%.

Assigning percentage values may involve heated arguments by the service chiefs. But this discussion is an internal, private matter for each side. Everybody involved speaks the same language, shares the same patriotic motives and is ultimately subordinate to the military discipline imposed by a single Head of State.

Choosing

It would be extraordinary if the values of usefulness chosen by one side were in exact agreement with the magnitude of threat felt by the other. Indeed we may expect that the weapons with accurate terminal guidance and short launch times, which are suitable for pre-emptive first strikes, will induce a feeling of threat in their victims which is much greater than the feeling of comfort they offer to their owners. On the other hand, inaccurate second-strike weapons are valuable deterrents and provide a large feeling of security, but do not pose a threat in proportion. It is precisely this *difference of opinion* which provides the incentive for the disarmament process and which ensures that both sides can believe that they have secured advantage.

The first reduction should be very small, say about 1%. Each side picks from the list of its opponent the most threatening items with total military percentage value not exceeding 1%. The selections may be announced simultaneously and small differences carried forward as credits for a second round.

If the Americans happened to decide that the SS-20 was the most serious threat they would request as a first move that 23 SS-20 missiles be dismantled. Meanwhile the Russians would pick the most threatening 1% of weapons from the American list. The Americans would be quite indifferent about the Russian choice because the numbers would have been chosen to make any 1% selection equal, in their view, to any other.

Both sides will think they benefit from this exchange by an amount which depends on the ratio of perceived threat removed to perceived protection lost. The process will seem exciting and even enjoyable to the selectors. They will be taking out the weapons which they see as posing the greatest threat and paying for this pleasure with reductions which, in their own judgement, are as indistinguishable as

a new approach

the dollar or rouble bills in their wallets.

The absolute, as opposed to the relative, magnitude of the reductions of each side, measured in terms of fire-power or lethality, will be greater for the power with the greater original armoury. But as each side argues that the other has the excess they can hardly object to this feature of the scheme.

Cheating

The problem of verification is common to all disarmament plans. A necessary assumption for any scheme is that both sides have reasonably accurate knowledge of the weapon systems of their opponents. This assumption is supported by several factors. Firstly, unknown weapons do not deter, and reluctance to disclose one's weapons can lead to accusations that one is preparing a surprise war-fighting system rather than a deterrent. Secondly, modern satellite techniques provide outstanding surveillance. Thirdly, the Soviet Union is now much more amenable to site inspections than in earlier years. If the reductions proceed by small, slow steps then neither side need fear that its national security has been greatly endangered if verfication goes wrong. However, if a side is sincere about its wish to disarm it can use the interpretation of verfication procedures to send messages about its sincerity and entice the other side to continue.

Either side may wish to distort the percentage values it declares. But because the sum total is always equal to a 100%, reduction in one area must necessarily mean an increase in another. Distortion is quite legitimate but the ploy may backfire and lead to the loss of good weapons at less than their true value. If one gives any credit to the intelligence services of one's opponent it will probably be best to make the military values as accurate a reflection of one's views as possible.

The scheme can cater for the pressure to modernise weapons. For example if Side A insists on the introduction of some new missiles it may do so provided that it also declares a military percentage value for them. Side B may then, without loss to its armoury, remove items to that same value from any part of Side A's inventory including the new ones. Side A will not want the new ones to be instantly lost and so will have to put a higher than true value on them. This rule would encourage the evolution of new weapons which provide high perceived security for low perceived threat — a most desirable feature.

Changing direction

It must be admitted that the scheme may be very slow and indeed might never achieve complete disarmament. But the safest number of nuclear weapons might not be zero and a slow scheme will give us time to decide what that number might be. We are at present facing a dangerous increase in both quantity and accuracy. An arrangement which slowed the rate of increase would be good. One which stopped it would be better. But one which reversed it by even the smallest amount would be best of all and would produce a very large relaxation in tension. Just as in levitation, the first millimetre will be the hardest!

Stephen Salter
Department of Mechanical Engineering
University of Edinburgh

May 1983

The trauma of surviving

It is a common experience for survivors of a major catastrophe to feel a deep sense of loneliness and a profound feeling of the futility of life. The psychological trauma deadens their behaviour as though they had been mentally anaesthetised without thought, without feeling.

When the outside world regains contact with the survivors, the behavioural paralysis relaxes its grip. For it is not only the material aid in the form of water, food, clothing and medicine that assists in their recovery, but the infectious vitality of human society which strengthens their will to live.

In a nuclear war there will be no regained contact, no surrounding human community, no world out there to count on. The survivors would remain in a deadened state, either alone or among others like themselves, largely without hope and vaguely aware that everyone and everything that once mattered to them had been destroyed. Thus survivors would experience not only the most extreme forms of individual trauma imaginable, but an equally severe form of collective trauma stemming from a rupture of the patterns of social existence.

Under these conditions such tasks as acquiring food and maintaining shelter would remain formidable for weeks, months, or even years. The band of survivors would be further reduced, not only by starvation and cold, but also by continuing exposure to radiation and disease.

The question so often asked: "Would the survivors envy the dead?" may turn out to have a simple answer. No, they would be incapable of such feeling. They would not so much envy as inwardly and outwardly resemble the dead.

Extracted from "Last Aid"[49] R. J. Lifton and K. Erikson.